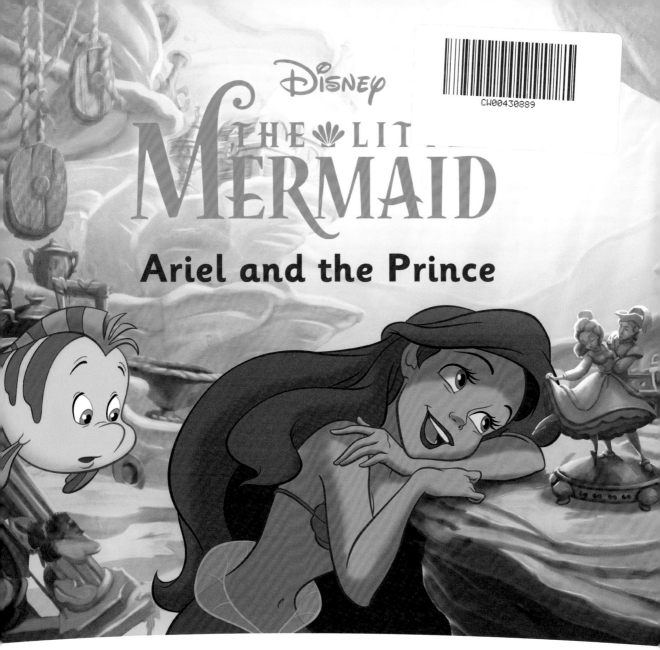

DISNEY

THE LITTLE MERMAID

Ariel and the Prince

Level 2

Re-told by: Kathryn Harper
Series Editor: Rachel Wilson

Before You Read

In This Book

Ariel　　　　King Triton　　　Prince Eric

Activity

Point and say. What lives in the ocean?

1 mermaid

2 dog

3 human

4 fish

5 fork

It's time to sing. The mermaids are ready.
King Triton is ready. But where is Ariel?

Ariel and Flounder are in an old ship.
She finds a fork. "What is it?" she asks.
... Oops! It's time to sing!

Ariel is late. King Triton is angry.
He wants her to stop playing with human
things. She's a mermaid.

Ariel loves human things. This is her
secret place. These are her human things.
Ariel looks up. What's that?

Ariel swims to the top of the water.
There's a ship. "It's beautiful," she thinks.

Ariel sees Prince Eric. One, two legs.
She sees a dog. One, two, three, four legs.
Ariel has no legs.

Suddenly, the clouds are dark.
It's windy. There's a big storm.
Oh, no! Prince Eric is falling!

Quickly, Ariel swims down.

She finds Prince Eric in the water.

She holds him and swims up, up, up.

Ariel takes Prince Eric to the beach.

She looks at his face.

Is he sleeping? Is he okay?

Prince Eric opens his eyes. Quickly, Ariel
leaves the beach, but she watches Prince Eric.
He's okay!

Ariel and Flounder swim back to the secret place. Ariel sings about the prince. She loves him!

King Triton finds Ariel's secret place.
Ariel doesn't want her mermaid's tail. She
wants legs. She wants to be with Prince Eric.

The king is very angry now.
"He's a human. You're a mermaid!" he says.

Ariel leaves her father.
"I'm not human *now*," she thinks.
"But I can find a way ..."

After You Read

1 **Read and answer Yes or No.**

1 Ariel is human.
2 Ariel loves Prince Eric.
3 Triton is Ariel's brother.
4 Prince Eric is a mermaid.
5 Ariel lives in the ocean.

2 **Put the story in order.**

a There is a storm.
b Ariel sees Prince Eric on the ship.
c Ariel helps Prince Eric.
d Prince Eric falls into the ocean.

3 **What do you think happens next?**

1 Ariel gets legs and finds Prince Eric.
2 Prince Eric lives in the ocean with Ariel.
3 Ariel lives on a ship.

Picture Dictionary

beach

fall

fork

human

love

mermaid

ship

cloud

storm

swim

Phonics

Say the sounds. Read the words.

E e

leg

red

I i

big

sit

Say the rhyme.

Ten big fish and six red fish
Swim quietly.
They don't have legs
To walk, you see.

Follow your dreams.

Find Out

How do you know it's a storm?

In a storm you can see dark clouds. The wind is strong and the rain is heavy. You can see lightning and you can hear thunder. It's loud!

lightning

Be careful in a storm ...

 Move away from trees.

 Go in the house.

 Move away from windows and doors.

Pearson Education Limited
KAO Two
KAO Park, Harlow,
Essex, CMI7 9NA, England
and Associated Companies throughout the world.

ISBN: 978-1-2923-4669-4

This edition first published by Pearson Education Ltd 2020

1 3 5 7 9 10 8 6 4 2

Set in Heinemann Roman Special, 19pt/28pt
Printed by Neografia, Slovakia

Published by Pearson Education Limited

Acknowledgments
123RF.com: Gino Santa Maria 18, NejroN 17, TAKASHI HONMA 16
Shutterstock.com: Dark Moon Pictures 20-21, Vladimir Melnikov 18

For a complete list of the titles available in the Pearson English Readers series, visit www.pearsonenglishreaders.com.

Alternatively, write to your local Pearson Education office or
to Pearson English Readers Marketing Department,
Pearson Education, KAO Two, KAO Park, Harlow, Essex, CMI7 9NA